THE WAYS OF NESTING BIRDS

THE WAYS

OF NESTING BIRDS

Raymond P. Holden

Illustrated by Grace DeWitt

DODD, MEAD & COMPANY
New York

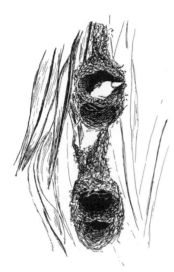

To my great-grandson,
Charles A. Hagebusch,
in the hope that when he
is old enough to be interested
in them there will still be
birds for him to study

ACKNOWLEDGMENTS

For help in the work which led to the production of this book I am especially indebted to Dr. Robert Cushman Murphy, who encouraged me, and to Dr. Dean Amadon, of the American Museum of Natural History, who allowed me to study the large collection of nests and eggs, including those which are not on exhibit at the Museum.

I have also to thank Dr. Clarence Cottam, of the Welder Wildlife Foundation, Sinton, Texas, whose hospitality permitted me to use the extraordinary facilities of the Foundation of which he is director for the completion of this book.

I am also under a debt of gratitude to the Baker Library of Dartmouth College, Hanover, New Hampshire, where I spent many exciting hours learning what other men have done with my subject.

I must also thank my wife, Barbara Holden, for very real help in the preparation of the material presented here.

CONTENTS

THE WAYS OF NESTING BIRDS

A WORD ABOUT BIRDS
AND THEIR NESTS

The chief concern of all living things is to survive and to produce young under conditions which will enable the young to survive. What we call life has been continuing on this earth for millions of years. As the surface of the earth has changed through cycles of fire, steam, water, and emerging and shifting land, the forms of life have had to change.

What was well able to survive in one epoch often failed and disappeared in another. Birds, which develop their young outside of their own bodies by laying eggs and warming them until they hatch, are descended from creatures akin to reptiles, most of which also lay eggs. Reptiles solved the egg problem in their own way long ago by using the sun's heat and decaying vegetable matter to provide the necessary warmth which their cold-blooded bodies lacked. In the process of developing into winged beings that could travel through the air, birds became warm-blooded, like the mammals. Feathers, found only in birds, made controlled flight possible, and also helped to preserve body heat.

Yet the bird, unlike the warm-blooded mammals, could not develop its young within its own body. In order to survive, many

13

birds have to produce as many as ten or fifteen eggs in a clutch (the name given to the set of eggs laid in one breeding period). The bird's body has no spare storage space, and it would greatly hamper a bird's flight to carry even the usual number of three to five eggs within itself if all of them developed at once. Birds can produce almost an unlimited number of eggs, but do not lay more in a clutch than the number of young birds which can be fed successfully in the nesting area. Eggs are laid one at a time, and each egg has to be put somewhere to wait until the rest are developed and laid and the heat of the parents' bodies applied to them. Some birds begin incubation with the first egg laid, but the majority do not start it until the last is laid, so that all eggs hatch at approximately the same time.

Birds have come up with widely varying answers to the problem of bringing up their young. Some mate for life; some have many different mates, even at the same time. Some birds stake out a territory of their own which they jealously protect from others of their kind. Some, among them many sea birds, prefer to breed in colonies with a multitude of others, defending as their own territory only the few feet immediately surrounding their breeding place. Most birds solve their problem by building a nest. Some use already available natural situations or nests others have built. Some do not feel the need of any nest and so make none.

The majority of perching birds do fashion or manufacture receptacles for their eggs and young, and these vary tremendously from the crude to the intricate. Some are made by simple arrangement, some by weaving or masonry or molding, a few by digging or sawing or chopping. Nests vary in size from as small as a half-dollar to those many feet across and weighing several tons. Most birds do not regard the nest as a home, though a few do return to it after the need for incubation has passed. Some return to the

14

same nest year after year, while others make new nests, sometimes more nests than they can possibly use in a season.

Most nests are stable, but a few are movable. Nests are built by various birds with and without tops, with side and bottom entrances, even with more than one compartment or with sealed-up rooms. Some birds seem to seek out the most difficult possible nesting site or to make the business of incubating the eggs as uncomfortable as possible. Sometimes there is only one egg, sometimes as many as fifteen or more. In some cases there is only one clutch in a season, in others as many as three. The young of some birds are born in Arctic temperatures and those of others in what might be regarded as intolerable heat. They are hatched in a short or a long time, with the devoted attention of one parent, or of both, or with neither of them seeming to care what happens to their offspring.

Is is commonly supposed that the nests of birds are as different from one another as their builders are. In a way this is so, but the differences, in the majority of birds, are not easy for the observer to see. Comparatively few birds build really distinctive nests of high-grade workmanship. The nests of scores of birds, even hundreds, are quite unknown even to ardent bird watchers. Some, however, are as beautiful as they are conspicuous.

The study of birds' nests can tell us much about the birds which build them, for the nest, far from being what human beings would call domestic architecture, is rather a part and extension of the bird's body, performing a bodily function which the feathered flying machine itself cannot perform. A bird's success in nesting largely determines whether or not that bird will survive. Since most living birds have existed on earth far longer than man, it is apparent that most forms of nest, or most efforts to produce young without having a nest, have been successful.

15

PRECOCIAL

ALTRICIAL

There are two different approaches to the business of producing a bird's young. Two rather unfamiliar words describe these approaches. There are *precocial* birds (from the word precocious, meaning highly developed at an early age) whose eggs, in proportion to the size of their bodies, are larger than usual and whose young, hatched from these eggs, are more nearly ready to cope with their world than the young of non-precocial birds. That means that precocial chicks, like the chick of the domestic hen, are born with their eyes open, a coat of down, and with workable legs. They can run and jump, although they cannot immediately fly.

The other group of birds are known as *altricial,* which simply means that the young are born naked, helpless, and blind, and unable to keep themselves warm. Most of the perching birds belong to this group, although there are borderline cases in which the young (as of the Palm Swift and the Fairy Tern), though not really able to shift for themselves, have to be able to cling to their birthplaces instead of squatting in a basket.

The accounts which follow will show a wide range of attempts at survival—all successful—and will, it is hoped, indicate some of the problems which a bird has to face if it is to rear its young. They may also perhaps suggest to the reader that it might be exciting to find out why these problems have arisen—why birds, in their many different ways, have met them as they have, and why a bird is not "free," as some poets seem to regard him, but in fact a slave to inherited habits of behavior.

THE BLUEBIRD

Birds that live in holes in trees do not always enjoy undisturbed possession of them, being frequently threatened by other birds as well as by mice and squirrels. The exquisite and soft-spoken Bluebird likes nothing so well as to nest in a hole in an apple tree, unless it is to use a birdhouse especially provided for it by human beings who like to remember that the Bluebird is supposed to signify happiness.

A pair of Bluebirds is very appealing to watch, the female popping in and out of the entrance to her hole and the male sitting calmly on a branch nearby and murmuring an all-but-inaudible song which is the very essence of gentle sweetness. Yet when there are young in the nest—which is little more than a heap of coarse twigs piled inside the hole—the approach of a flock of tree swallows, birds that seem to take their cousins, aunts, and uncles with them when they go house-hunting, is the signal for the male Bluebird to change into an entire air force by himself. He will fly a little way, do a couple of barrel rolls toward the swallows, and suddenly return to his place by the nest entrance as if nothing had happened. Before you know it, he is singing his little song again while the swallows soar, dive, and scream, but keep their distance.

18

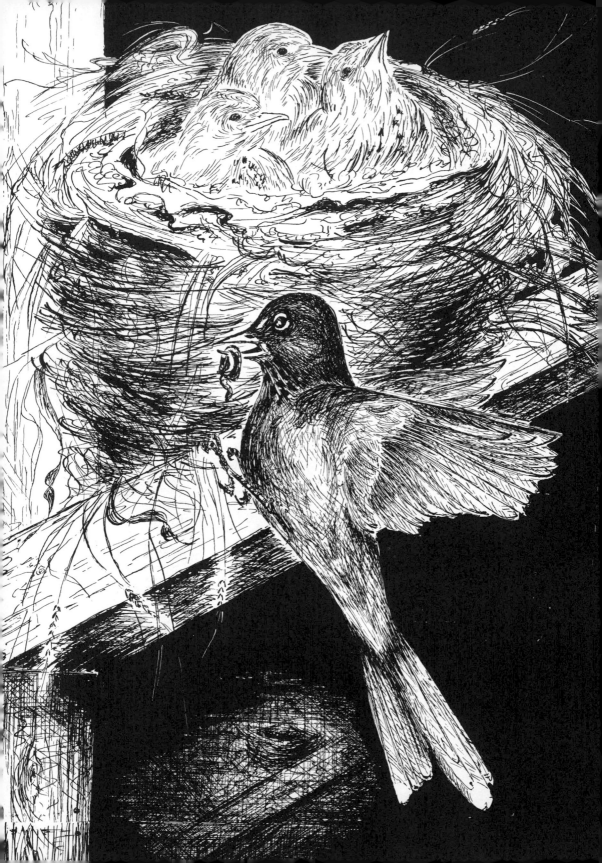

THE ROBIN

The American Robin, although it has a red breast, is quite unlike the British Robin Redbreast familiar in song and story, but is entitled to his name. The American Robin, one of our best-known birds, is really a thrush. This busy bird lives on earthworms and fruit—and many enemies of fruit such as cutworms, grubs, and wireworms.

The Robin builds a nest like that of no other thrush, and it is a sturdy, practical structure rather than a work of art. It is made of coarse grasses and other vegetable material molded into a large cup and held together by a lining of mud. The mud cup is lined with fine grass. The gray-cheeked thrush only occasionally uses mud in its nest, but the Robin always does.

The Robin likes, apparently, to be near the habitations of men but, as a nest builder, is usually rather careless, perhaps because of a failure to understand the strange ways of men. Robins have been known to build their nests on the carriage of a sawmill directly in the path of the saw. Sometimes the Robin's nest is built inside a barn on a rafter and sometimes the builder forgets what part of the rafter the nest was started on. Failing to find the original, the Robin starts another nest within sight of the first. Frequently the nest is not built high enough in a tree or shrub to be out of reach of cats and so gets torn down. If that happens, the Robin does not give up and say, "What's the use?" This bird simply starts another nest and lays a new clutch of eggs.

21

THE BALTIMORE ORIOLE

This delightful bird of the eastern United States has no partic-ular connection with the city of the same name. His striking colors of brilliant orange and black happen to be the colors of the English lord from whom the Maryland city took its name. Neither is the Oriole an Oriole. He is only called that because he makes a nest similar to the European Oriole's. Actually he belongs to the family which includes the cowbird, the blackbirds, the grackles, and the bobolink, none of whom are fancy nest-makers, the cowbird mak-ing none at all.

The Baltimore Oriole makes the most remarkable nest of any of our common North American birds. This bird, without ever having seen anyone build a nest, goes about building as if it had spent four years in a school of Oriole engineering. The Baltimore Oriole first selects a proper position in a tree, preferably in the high branch of an elm, choosing a branch which has three or four small stems springing from it close together. The structure is begun by looping strands of material—any long material will do, grass, worsted, or strips of bark—over one stem after another and letting them hang down while the rim is finished. Next, the bird weaves pieces into the sides by pushing and pulling, sometimes success-fully and sometimes not. When the sides are done the Oriole picks up the lower ends of the hanging strands and weaves them into a bottom. To make an Oriole's nest takes from twenty-five to thirty hours of actual work.

THE RED-WINGED BLACKBIRD

The Redwing, or Red-winged Blackbird, who belongs to the same family as the splendid Baltimore oriole, is rather splendid himself in a quiet way. The male bird is about as different from his mate as could be imagined. The female is a dull-looking creature of inconspicuous brown and rusty black with a sprinkling of white showing through here and there.

The male Redwing is not as independent as some birds who are handsomer than their mates. He does not do much about nest-building, but is not too proud to carry material. In the Redwing's case, the material is coarse marsh grass, weeds of any kind and, for lining, animal hair—horse or cow if it can be found. This is woven into a deep, loose cup fastened between reeds or cattails in or near water, sometimes on the ground. The mother bird does all the hatching and brooding of her four eggs, but the male Redwing does bring food, though less regularly than the mother bird.

He is fairly good about the matter of cleaning the nest. This is very important to nesting birds. The droppings of young birds in a nest from which they do not move for more than ten days could be very troublesome as well as unpleasant. Mites and other tiny insects are always present in nests and always dangerous. Material which would encourage their presence has to be kept down, lest they destroy the nestlings. Both parents work regularly at cleaning the nest.

THE BLUE JAY

One of the commonest birds of the eastern states is the noisy and often comical Blue Jay. He is, in bright light, spectacular in coloring, apparently bright blue, tinged with purple and with a black forehead and a necklace of black on his breast. In spite of his brilliance, on gray days and when seen without direct sunlight on him, he looks gray, or even black. This is because his color is not true pigment but a matter of reflected light.

The Blue Jay has a great variety of notes, which range from a loud scream to a soft creaky gurgle. One of his calls is often mistaken for the call of the red-shouldered hawk. This Jay is a rough and rowdy creature with an enormous appetite for eggs—including those of his own kind—acorns (which he can swallow without bothering to remove the shell), sunflower seeds, corn, berries and, in summer, insects.

As might be expected of such a character, the nest could hardly be described as delicate or beautiful. It is usually a coarse bulky lump, made of twigs, grass stems, pieces of string, or broken roots. It is built in almost any kind of tree—evergreens seem to be preferred—at a height of from four or five to thirty or forty feet. The Blue Jay's young are naked and helpless when they are born, not even opening their eyes for eight or nine days. They are at first—like reptiles and all altricial birds—unable to produce a constant body temperature and have to be warmed by their parents until their "thermostats" begin to work and they become warm-blooded.

26

THE SONG SPARROW

The Song Sparrow is so common throughout the United States that, but for his song, he might be overlooked as "just another bird." He is, however, a remarkable little being. The gathering together into a single dark patch of the brown streaks on his breast makes him easy to identify. His song varies somewhat according to locality and also from youth to maturity. He is a belligerent creature, strongly inclined to defend the territory he has chosen as his home base and rather tough with his spouse—to whom he is not always faithful. The Song Sparrow certainly does not mate for life, no matter how pure his song may sound.

The Song Sparrow's nesting habits are somewhat irregular. It is usually, though perhaps not always, the female which does the nest-building and she is by no means inflexible in her choice of sites. Sometimes the nest is made in deep grass, sometimes on fairly exposed hummocks, and sometimes several feet off the ground in a bush. The nest is formed of coarse grass, leaves, weeds, and strips of bark. It is sometimes heavy and with a deep cup lined with animal hair, and sometimes shallow and relatively insecure and lined only with grass. The Song Sparrow shows qualities of individuality which many other birds seem to lack.

29

THE HOUSE WREN

It is the male House Wren who starts nest-building. To be on the safe side, he begins not one but several nests. He will raise two families in a season, though not necessarily with the same mate.

The House Wren, a small brown bird with a thin bill and a habit of slanting his tail upward, is found all over the United States. In the winter, he migrates southward, and when he returns in the spring he lays claim by his song and by his vigorous defense against other birds to roughly an acre of territory. Within this area, he locates cavities appropriate for nesting holes. He may consider anything from a simple hole in a tree trunk to a pocket in a scarecrow's trousers appropriate, though he often takes advantage of man-made birdhouses. To each of these, he brings twigs and sticks. When a female enters his territory, she inspects all of the nests and indicates that she finally accepts her mate by bringing to the nest of her choice material with which to line it—feathers, straw, sometimes shiny snakeskins.

Thirteen days after the pinkish-salmon eggs are laid, anywhere from five to seven small Wrens are hatched. During the fifteen days the young remain in the nest and for another thirteen days after they leave it, both parents care for them. When the young have left the nest, the male clears it of all lining material and debris, leaving only his original twigs as a base for a possible nest for a second brood.

30

THE COWBIRD

The Cowbird has a bad reputation. She is not one of those birds that can do without a nest, but she has invented a way of not making one, and still getting her eggs taken care of. The fact that she makes other birds work for her is what has given her the bad reputation, although that is rather unreasonable of human beings as we do not know that birds have any opinion at all about industriousness.

A pair of Cowbirds picks out an area in which they would like to spend the breeding season. When they are mated they look about to see who else has chosen the same area. When they find a suitable bird busy making a nest, they watch and wait. When the nest is finished and the maker of it away, the female Cowbird pops into the nest and lays an egg. She then goes away as if nothing had happened and in the course of a week finds enough other nests to accommodate her other eggs, usually four or five. When the nest-builder returns she is not entirely sure she did not lay that egg herself. She may throw it out or cover it up with more nest material. This is a chance the Cowbird takes. Usually the nest-builder lays her own eggs right beside the Cowbird's and incubates them all.

The Cowbird's egg hatches in a shorter time than that of most of the birds whose nests she uses. This means that when the foster parents start feeding, the Cowbird chick gets fed first and is out of the nest and away before the others—unless, as sometimes happens, the intruding nestling has already pushed the rightful owners out.

THE YELLOW WARBLER

This pretty little bird, sometimes called wild canary or summer yellow-bird, is quite common in North America. There is no other of our birds more completely yellow.

The yellowness does not extend to the bird's character, however. He has a constant worry on his mind but you would never know it, for although his song is not, like the true canary's, of operatic quality, it is hearty and cheerful. It is his fate to be one of the favorite victims of the cowbird, but he is one of the few that doesn't take the cowbird's imposition lying down. When the female Yellow Warbler finds, as she all too often does, a cowbird's egg in her nest she promptly builds a new nest on top of the egg, instead of merely throwing it out as some birds do. She has been known to do this at least three times in succession, rather spoiling the proportions of her beautiful little nest but certainly discouraging the cowbird.

Her nest is always neatly and carefully made in the crotches of the branches of small trees. It is woven of a silvery gray grass mixed with weed fiber, plant and fern down, the silk from caterpillars' cocoons, horse hair, and an occasional feather. The tiny eggs, usually from three to five, are whitish marked with brown and lilac blotches. They are laid in May or June, depending on the locality. Like most tree-dwelling birds, the young are born naked and helpless.

THE PILEATED WOODPECKER

Nature tries every imaginable kind of experiment with life and many unimaginable ones. The successful ones result in creatures which survive, and the unsuccessful ones in creatures which some-day disappear. Consider the Woodpecker. His great bill and strong neck muscles would not help a robin dig worms. They do, however, help him get grubs and beetles out of trees which would give a robin a hard time.

The Pileated Woodpecker is a huge bird, almost as big as a crow and as black, but with white over his bright eyes and down the sides of his neck and under his wings and a flowing red cockade on his head. This splendid bird lives in deep old North American forests where he uses his enormous bill as a chisel to get at the insects and grubs by boring deep in the great trees. The Pileated Woodpecker can cut out chips as big as a man's hand without getting a headache. His ability to do this and so make enormous oblong holes in trees makes it possible for him to create cavities big enough to nest in. In excavating he makes a sound like a rivet-ing machine working on a skyscraper. Sometimes the nest holes are seven or eight inches high and five to seven inches wide and extend for as much as two feet into the tree. Here the female, who helps her mate chop out the hole, lays three to six large eggs and has a very comfortable time incubating them.

THE CACTUS WREN

Anyone who has ever touched its sharp, prickly spines might be pardoned for regarding the cholla cactus of our Southwest as the least likely of nesting sites. Yet the Cactus Wren, largest of the Wren family, chooses it if he can, regarding other shrubs and bushes as second-best.

The Cactus Wren's nest—or more properly his nests, for both male and female build nests constantly—are homes rather than, as with most birds, simply temporary shelters for raising young. All through the year Cactus Wrens retire to nests to roost at sunset, one bird to a nest, and since the nests are often destroyed by time, weather, and other birds, they must spend considerable hours repairing them and building new ones. The Cactus Wren does not migrate, so presumably he has ample leisure for this useful occupation. Cactus thorns do not seem to bother him at all. He picks his way slowly among them.

The breeding nest, in which several reddish-brown eggs are laid, is three feet to eight feet above the ground. Shaped somewhat like a long-necked pouch or bottle, about a foot in length, the nest is slanted downward, with the neck, which serves as entrance and vestibule, facing outward from the cholla. Normally the nesting material is twigs, dried grasses, and plant fibers matted together, the inside being lined with soft material, preferably feathers. Where civilization has crept into the desert, chicken feathers are the favorite lining, and the one-and-a-half-inch-thick walls may include such items as newspapers, tissue, cotton, string, or rope. Two or three broods are raised in a season.

THE RUBY-THROATED HUMMINGBIRD

The Hummingbird is found only in the Americas, mostly in subtropical and tropical countries. One variety, the Ruby-throat, is common throughout the eastern United States. Everything about this bird except his speed and his appetite is miniature. He can stand still in the air, dart up, down, and away like a bullet, and can even fly backwards. Although his food is mostly flower nectar and small insects, he has been known to kill frogs, spiders, hawk moths, and dragonflies.

The Hummingbird's nest is built on a high, firm branch many feet above the ground, preferably near water. The base is constructed of flakes of lichen and the scales of small plant buds cemented together with sticky, silky threads gathered from spider webs. The sides are built up of the same material, including the down of whatever plants may have bloomed by nesting time or the silky fluff of last year's milkweed and old goldenrod or cattails. The nests are very hard to find, being about as round as a silver dollar and barely an inch and a quarter high, and looking very much like a warty growth on the branch. The cup, which is carefully smoothed and rounded by the breast of the tiny female—the male does not do much about building—is barely half an inch deep and holds two tiny white eggs. The nest is so built that it is used for more than one season, and the female keeps repairing it even during the time she is incubating her eggs.

THE GOLDFINCH

As a rule, tropical birds are more brilliantly colored than those found in cooler places. It is also often true that where the male bird is very different from the female and wears fancy colors, he is likely to be half-hearted about helping to build the nest and incubate the eggs. This is not really true of that exquisite and gay bird, the American Goldfinch—perhaps because his pride in his fancy dress is cooled by the change he undergoes in winter, when he discards his lemon-yellow and black suit and puts on an olive-gray costume very much like the colors the female wears all year round.

The Goldfinch makes a tiny but very compact and tidy nest of thin, hairlike grass, moss, and bits of plant fiber, which is lined with silky down from several kinds of seed pods. The Goldfinch, being a seed-eater, is not so dependent on migration as are insect-eating birds. He does not, therefore, have to nest as early in order to get the young ones ready for the trip south before the supply of insects gives out. This means that even in the northern part of his range, which runs up into Canada, he can afford to wait until milkweed, fireweed, thistledown, and clematis have bloomed and turned into seeds. Without their silky down he would not regard a nest as a nest. There is always some kind of plant down cushioning the three to six bluish-white eggs in a Goldfinch's nest.

THE CLIFF SWALLOW

The Cliff Swallow, common throughout the United States, does not always nest in cliffs. In fact, he is often mistaken for the barn swallow by those who do not realize the difference in appearance, because he likes to nest in and on barns. He is the same steel-blue color as the barn swallow, but has a whitish forehead, a gray instead of brown and buff breast, a white belly, and a short tail.

The Cliff Swallow has come up with something unusual in nest design. He likes to live, as most swallows do, not too far from others of his kind, but he makes an individual nest in which the female lays her four or five white, brown-marked eggs. The Cliff Swallow's nest is really a kind of pottery jug shaped like a gourd or fat bottle in which the actual nesting material, consisting of wool when it can be had, grass, moss, and feathers, is placed. The jug itself is made of mud pellets carefully pressed together and shaped almost as if it had been done on a potter's wheel. The pellets are apparently mixed with a little sticky saliva while being carried to the nesting site. They are carefully attached to the growing circle of mud while the bird clings with his feet to the sharp rafter on which the nest is being made. These nests are always made under some overhang or inside a barn so that rain will not wash them away.

44

THE BROWN THRASHER

THE BROWN THRASHER

The Brown Thrasher somewhat resembles a large elongated thrush, but actually belongs to the same family as the wrens and the catbirds. He is a striking bird with a song like a catbird's or mockingbird's. Thrashers have an unmistakable bill which is long and curved. In fact, the scientific name for the Brown Thrasher found in the eastern part of North America means "sickle-nose." He likes to nest in a thicket or the edge of a wood. His song is a hodgepodge of all sorts of sounds he has heard, which he strings together and repeats for emphasis. He sings high; he sings low. Like the catbird, he can mew like a cat or yap like a dog.

He is almost as independent in nest-building as in singing. He sometimes builds on the ground or near it, sometimes in low bushes, sometimes part way up in trees. The nest is no great work of art. The Thrasher is too exuberant to be a careful weaver. He rather throws things together to make a nest which is sometimes not more than a rough platform to hold the clutch of three to six eggs, which are bluish or grayish white speckled with brown. Even when the nest is sketchy it is usually lined with rootlets, leaves, or fine grass. Yet he is not one to use twigs just because that is what Thrashers are supposed to do. There is a Brown Thrasher's nest in the American Museum of Natural History which is made of strips and curls of stainless steel picked up outside a New Jersey car factory.

THE MAGPIE

It is probably safe to assume that in most birds the good out-weighs the bad. There is one bird, the Magpie, found in many parts of the Old World, in China, and in the northwestern part of North America, which has had a bad if romantic reputation for as long as men can remember. He is usually spoken of as a thief and has found a place in literature by stealing jewelry for the loss of which innocent human beings have been blamed. Certainly the Magpie has a taste for bright objects, with which he likes to ornament his nest, and since no one has told him that there is such a thing as ownership of private property, he could not properly be called "bad." The Magpie is at times a trifle bloodthirsty and perhaps cruel—he kills chickens, young sheared lambs, and even attacks sick cattle. Yet we have to balance against this the fact that the greater part of his diet consists of insects, large and small, which are enemies of man and his crops.

The Magpie makes a large nest, sometimes in the tops of trees, as big as a bushel fruit basket. It consists of large twigs, dried grass, and weeds, with a lining of finer material often plastered with mud. The entrance is at one side of the mass. The Magpie likes to nest near others of his kind and is very noisy about it. The female Magpie lays seven or more grayish or greenish-white eggs dotted and blotched with brown or dull purple.

Tame Magpies can be taught to talk, but not in a way that can tell us anything about Magpie thoughts. Their sounds are purely imitative.

THE MAGPIE

THE OVENBIRD

Birds are divided into families according to the structure of their bodies rather than according to the structure of their nests. If this were not so, the Ovenbird would not be considered a member of the warbler family, which he is. He lives in the woods and is almost never found anywhere else. He spends most of his time on the ground. He is somewhat larger than most warblers but much less gaily colored, his general appearance being streaky brown with an orange-brown crown edged in black. Many people who have walked in the woods have heard his loud and insistent but melodious song which says, "Cheater, cheater, cheater!" Some insist that the Ovenbird says, "Teacher, teacher, teacher!" which of course is not the same thing.

The Ovenbird blends perfectly with the ground, is a quick and clever dodger, and always makes his nest on the ground. Many birds who are ground-nesters lay eggs which blend with the surroundings and so are hard to see. The Ovenbird, whose four to six eggs are white blotched with brown and lilac, builds a nest unlike that of any other warbler, out of leaves and leaf stems, moss, and small vines. The unusual thing about the nest is that it has a roof made by bending over the stems of the sides and adding a thatch of leaves so that when finished it resembles, if rather roughly, an old-fashioned outdoor oven.

THE PHOEBE

The Phoebe, which has no song except a frequent recital of his name, is a rather drab little bird. He is a flycatcher who sits on a post apparently paying no attention to anything and suddenly picks himself up, darts out, and returns to his post with a fly or moth or grasshopper in his beak. This he immediately delivers to his nest, which resembles a small bird pie out of which five yellow-bordered mouths protrude. As the male and female in turn bring more and more insects, the pie swells day by day until suddenly it bursts and five little Phoebes, who may have heard about flying but never tried it, go off in all directions as if they had never heard of sitting still.

Long ago when there were no convenient houses, Phoebes used to make their nests in rocks and ledges, never very far from water. Now, though they still like to be near water, they usually build in barns, on porches, under the eaves of houses, or in any somewhat protected place. The reason for being near water is that the Phoebe is a mason and cements his nest together with little pellets of mud and saliva. He makes the main structure of the nest of grass and moss, reinforced with mud and lined with fine rootlets and animal hair.

A pair of Phoebes will use the same nest year after year with little alteration and raise at least two broods in one season—unless, as very often happens, they build on sliding garage doors which cannot be pushed upward without destroying the bird's work. If human beings do not enjoy having their doors spattered with mud and remove the nest from which it drips, they will have to do so three or four times before the Phoebe is convinced she picked the wrong place.

54

THE CHICKADEE

The Chickadee, which is familiar to people in the northeastern part of the United States, is one of the friendliest and most energetic of birds, so energetic that he has to be eating most of the time. Wherever there are bird feeders in winter you will find the Chickadee, but he is not dependent upon them. There are always old tops of goldenrod sticking above the snow and the tall stalks of the evening primrose rattling in the wind. He is as friendly and enthusiastic at forty below zero in deep snow as he is in summer.

When spring comes the Chickadee is far from exhausted by the rigors of winter. He is quite capable of chopping out a hole in a tree in which to make his nest, if the tree is just a little bit on the rotten side. If he uses ready-made holes, it is merely because he is clever and in a hurry. He spends quite a lot of time building a nest inside the hole, which is more than most hole-dwellers do. The Chickadee collects moss, small bits of wool or down, plant fiber, hair, and even fur, and makes a very snug and cushiony receptacle for the five to eight white, lightly-marked eggs. The stuff is worked very fine, and simply matted down without any attempt at weaving. The Chickadee may use as much as a quart of material to hold the eggs, all of which could rest comfortably in a tablespoon.

THE CRESTED FLYCATCHER

It is very difficult in many cases to identify a bird's nest without seeing the bird that made it either doing so or sitting on it. Birds, although they stick fairly close to inherited ideas in the type and shape of nests they make, show considerable variation in the materials they use. The story is told of a pair of English chaffinches which were taken in the form of eggs from their English nest to New Zealand, twelve thousand miles away, and artificially hatched. There, never having seen a chaffinch's nest, they mated, built a nest, and laid eggs. The nest was exactly like an English chaffinch's nest except that it used New Zealand materials.

The American Crested Flycatcher, which is common in the eastern United States, is a rather large Flycatcher, a little smaller than a robin. This noisy bird builds a nest in a hole in a tree. The nest, in which from three to six buff-colored, dark-splotched eggs are laid, is made of grasses, coarse weeds, feathers, and small leaves. It is remarkable how often it has been reported that the Crested Flycatcher includes a shed snakeskin in its nest. This addition is so common as to seem something more than accidental. Yet it is interesting to note that this Flycatcher is not so conservative that he will hesitate to use a discarded cellophane cigar wrapper as the next best thing to a snakeskin. It perhaps would not fool a snake, but it satisfies the bird.

59

THE RED-EYED VIREO

The Vireos are a charming tribe of small birds found only in the Western hemisphere. The commonest of them in eastern North America is the friendly Red-eyed Vireo. He is an insect-eater, who does not, as a rule, catch his food in the air the way flycatchers do. Instead, he walks busily about in trees examining the undersides of leaves and crevices in the bark, where he never fails to find caterpillars, spiders, beetles, aphids, and flies.

The Vireos, as a family, are remarkable among bird families for the fact that there is very little variation in the type of nest which each variety makes. They are all skillful weavers and the nest of the Red-eyed Vireo is typical. It is a beautifully symmetrical cup, almost always hung from a fork of a small branch, carefully fastened to the stem of each side of the fork. It is usually from two-and-a-half to three inches across and from one-and-a-half to two inches deep. The sides, being carefully woven, are quite thin. The material used is somewhat varied, according to what is available, but it includes grass, small leaves, thin strips of birch-bark, paper, parts of cocoons, and pieces of the gray paper-like shell of wasps' nests. It is always smooth and neat and, unlike the lumps of stuff thrown together by some birds, gives the impression that loving care has gone into its making. The three or four tiny eggs are white with a little faint speckling at the larger end.

THE ROSE-THROATED BECARD

The South American cotinga family includes the musical bell bird and the golden cock-of-the-rock, as large as a parrot. The cotingas have a cousin, the Rose-throated Becard who is, very rarely, found nesting in southern Arizona. This unusual bird was first found in the 1880's and not seen again for sixty years. It has now been established that he nests in the usually dry watershed of the Santa Cruz River near the Mexican border.

The Rose-throated Becard is only a little larger than a sparrow but she lays as many as six eggs, which are unusually large for a bird of her size, and all together weigh three-fifths of the total weight of the bird herself. The Becard seems to have a passion for doing things on a grand scale. She makes her nest in cottonwood trees far out on the end of a branch where the stem is not more than a quarter of an inch thick. The nest is made of grasses and strips of cottonwood bark and is matted together to make a large, irregular mass sometimes two-and-a-half feet long and fifteen or sixteen inches wide. There is a three-inch entrance hole six inches from the bottom, leading to a nest cavity, about five inches by seven, in the center of the mass. The Becard must enjoy this sort of nest-building, for she will build a new nest within two or three feet of last year's, rather than use the old one.

THE SHRIKE

There are two varieties of Shrike in the United States, the Northern and the Loggerhead, but the average person would have quite a bit of trouble telling them apart at the distance at which they are usually seen. This bird has a habit which has caused him to be regarded as a criminal, although since he is just trying, like other birds, to get along, he probably would not understand why. His scientific name, *Lanius*, means "butcher." He is called this because in addition to his natural taste for such things as grass-hoppers, he likes to eat other small birds and even mice and snakes, and finds it convenient to store what he kills by impaling them on thorns and sharp twigs near his nest, just as we might put meat in our freezer or refrigerator. Perhaps the Shrike should be called the thrift bird rather than the butcher bird.

The Shrike's nest is a well-constructed bowl of twigs, thorny vines, grasses, strips of bark, and plant fibers, with a lining of softer grass. In this the female lays from three to five milk-white eggs marked with spots of brown and lavender. You would not expect a bird with such a sinister reputation to sing like a choir boy, but the Shrike does. He is a somewhat gurgling and rather inattentive choir boy, but a singer none the less.

64

THE PINE GROSBEAK

The Grosbeak family is remarkable for the beauty and variety of its members, which are among the most gaily colored of North American birds. The Evening Grosbeak looks more like a tropical bird than a northerner.

The Pine, or Canadian, Grosbeak is a beautiful, rosy bird belonging to the winter. Pine Grosbeaks are seldom seen in the United States except in wintertime. Though a few may stay to nest in northern Maine or perhaps in the mountains of Colorado, it is still winter in the Canadian woods when most of them return to build their nests in evergreen trees often covered with frost and snow.

Their nests are six to seven inches in diameter, and three-and-a-half to four inches deep, built in branches of pine, spruce, or balsam, not far above the ground. The outer shell of the nest is made from small twigs and rootlets closely and skillfully woven together, and the inside is lined with fine grasses, lichens, or bark strips.

The female, who is a subdued green in contrast to her mate's brighter rose, lays three or four beautiful eggs, of a light greenish-blue, but splotched and spotted with darker shades from lilac to brown. The touch of winter has not really gone from the north woods when the young Pine Grosbeaks are hatched in the latter part of May or early June. The nests and young of this interesting bird are not frequently observed, since not many people find their way through snow-laden Canadian woods at that season of the year.

THE BROWN CREEPER

A very peculiar little bird of Canada and the Northeast, seldom seen even by those who are looking for it, is the Brown Creeper. It has a long thin bill with a slight downward curve which is very valuable for picking insects out of bark. The Creeper is a mottle of various shades of brown with highlights of buff and white. He is very hard to see against the bark of the trees which he spends most of his time inspecting, beginning at the bottom and working jerkily upward. He is not at all a sociable bird and is a very silent one. He does murmur faintly to himself sometimes, but you would have to be within a few feet of him to hear the sound and it is not easy to get within a few feet of him.

His favorite nesting place is behind a flap of bark which has curled away from a rotten or dying trunk or stump, usually of pine or spruce, or one that has been torn loose by wind—a place in which neither man nor beast would expect to find a nest. The nest itself is not exactly a prize example of the weaver's art. It consists of a heap of twigs, bark chips, moss, and sometimes feathers, loosely held together by tangles of sticky cobweb. The five or six eggs are marked almost like the bird itself, with mottled brown on buff.

68

THE WOOD DUCK

The Wood Duck has been called the most beautiful of our wild fowl, the male being spectacular in his iridescent hues of purple, violet, red, green, and bronze mixed with black and white. Apart from his beauty, the Wood Duck is interesting as the only member of the river and pond duck family that nests in trees, never on the ground. It will occasionally nest in an abandoned barn or shed, but usually in some natural hole in a tree and never very far from the water. It is quite partial to nesting boxes, put up by man in the hope of encouraging nesting and so increasing its numbers, as it is a much sought-after game bird. The tree cavities used by Wood Ducks are usually from twenty to fifty feet above the ground and contain no nesting material other than down from the female's breast, unless there happen to be some chips in the cavity when taken over. The duck brings nothing to it.

The height of the cavity creates a problem for the young, who leave the nest before they can fly, though not before they can walk and swim. The problem is met by the courage of ignorance. The babies do not know what the ground is like, so out they go when the mother calls, bouncing like balls but apparently uninjured even when the ground is hard. Peeping noisily, they pick themselves up and scurry after their mother toward the water, dodging under leaves to avoid being seen by hawks.

THE SWAN

The Swan is a very large, very graceful, and beautiful bird which has romantic associations. Most varieties are practically pure white. They have the habit of remaining mated for life and of being very devoted to their young and their companions. They breed in northern Europe and arctic North America, flying south in winter in perfect V-shaped flocks of from ten to twenty birds.

Both the European and American Swans are rather messy and careless nest-builders and their nesting habits have suggested to students of bird life an idea which may help to explain the origin of nest-building. The male Swan, during the season when he is courting, has the habit of moving slowly about plucking bits of reed and grass and even sticks and flinging them backwards, over his shoulder as it were. It is thought by some that since the female is interested in what a male does while courting her, she tries to keep romance alive by picking up grass and reeds herself and heaping them up about her, eventually laying her eggs in the middle of the pile and discovering, perhaps not entirely to her surprise, that it provides a handy place in which to incubate them. Certainly the female Swan could easily hatch her three to six eggs in a hummock of grass without any nest if she wished.

THE PIED-BILLED GREBE

The Pied-billed Grebe is found all over the United States, as a permanent resident on the Pacific coast and in the South, and as a nesting and breeding bird in the North from April to October. This Grebe lives in small ponds and shallow, watery marshes, inlets, and bays, wherever there is an abundance of shore plants and where small fish, crayfish, snails, and water insects are found.

The Pied-billed Grebe, which is a rather stocky little bird with a short, black-ringed bill which is higher than it is wide, builds its nests among reeds and aquatic grasses, and plans it so that it will float easily with the parent bird and her young in it. The nest is made of the stems of water plants, which are often hollow and therefore light, though even algae and sometimes a little mud are used. The floating nest is usually fastened to standing rushes or reeds and, in shallow water, is sometimes built up from the bottom of the pond. The brooding parent always covers the eggs with grass when leaving the nest even for a short time. The young, when hatched, are very active (precocial) and climb all over themselves and their mother, who broods them among her back feathers instead of by sitting on them.

74

THE EMPEROR PENGUIN

The Emperor Penguin stands three to three-and-a-half feet high and has a chest measurement of as much as fifty inches. Some weigh as much as ninety pounds. The only thing birdlike about the Emperor is his feathers. He can "fly" only in water, where he does very well.

He lives in the Antarctic and he lives on sea creatures like. squids. The Antarctic summer, when the water near shore is free of ice and capable of accommodating a squid-hunting Penguin, is very short. As it takes two months to hatch a Penguin's egg and another five for the chick to grow big enough to take care of itself, the egg must be laid in Antarctic midwinter. There are no twigs, grasses, or even pebbles or mud available in Antarctica in winter, so the Penguin cannot build a nest. Also there is no food. What does the Penguin do for a nest and to keep the egg warm?

The female lays the egg, passes it to the male, who rests it between his two feet, covered by a feathered flap of skin which makes him look as if his underwear had fallen down. He stands, in a crowd of others like him, with the egg balanced on his feet, for two months in bitter wind, with the temperature from forty to seventy degrees below zero. During this time he does not eat a thing and loses from thirty to forty pounds. When the egg finally hatches he feeds the chick on a secretion from his own throat until the females, who have been fattening on squid far out on the ice edge, return to take over.

In the Emperor Penguin's case, the nest is truly an extension of the body of the bird, although it is the father's rather than the mother's body.

76

THE PUFFIN

THE PUFFIN

The Puffin is distinguished by the tremendously thick, brilliantly colored bill both sexes display. This remarkable bill, part of which is shed after the breeding season, serves not only to attract the opposite sex but to dig nests and to transport fish, sometimes as many as twenty at a time.

Puffins spend their winters in the North Atlantic, as far north as there is open water. In spring they return to long-established breeding colonies on northern islands and along rocky coasts. Sometimes called "sea parrots," Puffins are sociable, curious, and affectionate, showing their devotion by the frequent rubbing together of their gaudy bills. Once a pair chooses a nesting place—perhaps they'll dig a new burrow, as much as two feet in length, or repair an existing one, or take one over from a rabbit—they may line it with dry grass or a few feathers. In the only United States colonies—two "down east" islands off the coast of Maine—they often nest in natural burrows under shallow rocks.

For forty days, both parents incubate the single egg. The down-covered chick which is born has a perfectly ordinary-looking, thin bill. For another forty days after the chick hatches, his parents will bring him the fish he needs to grow. Then they will desert him completely. After several days alone in the nest, the independent little Puffin will, one night, walk out, head directly toward the sea, plunge in, and be off on his own.

80

THE EIDER

Nearly everyone has heard of eider down as the name of something typical of softness and warmth, but not everyone knows what it is, where it comes from, or how it gets into quilts, pillows, and sleeping bags. The Eider is a large and unusual duck found in the northern part of the world. The American species was very nearly extinct not many years ago, but is now at least partly protected and is becoming more numerous.

The most remarkable thing about the Eider is that under its breast feathers it wears a coat of soft, wool-like down. Although the Eider's nest is merely a matted heap of seaweed, sticks, and chips of driftwood, leaves, and grass, the cup at its center, in which the eggs are laid, is always thickly lined with down which the mother duck plucks from her breast.

In Iceland, in addition to being illegal, it is considered a horrible crime to kill an Eider. In fact, the wild ducks are farmed by building stone corrals inside which they are encouraged to build their nests. When the nest is finished and the down lining is in place, part—but never all—of the down is gathered. The mother bird then plucks more from her breast and relines the nest. Part of this second lining is again gathered, but there is usually enough left to satisfy the bird and the practice does her no harm. Thirty-five or forty nests will provide a pound of down, which brings a very high price.

THE EIDER

DEWITT

THE KINGFISHER

The Kingfisher is a beautiful, strikingly marked bird known to all who live in the country areas of almost any land. His big crested head and chunky body are never seen very far from water for, as his name suggests, he lives on fish. He can often be seen sitting on a branch over a stream, seeming to be looking straight ahead. Suddenly, however, he will drop from the branch as if shot and disappear under water, only to come up with a fish, sometimes half his own size, in his mouth.

The Kingfisher is not a weaver. He builds no nest, but to raise a family either uses a ready-made hole in a tree or digs one for himself in the earth or sand of a stream bank. For this unbirdlike task he uses his strong bill, the feathered "hands" which are his wings, and his strong feet. He digs on a level, straight into the bank for sometimes as much as four or five feet, sometimes more. At the far end of this burrow, which is about as wide as a man's fist, the female Kingfisher lays from five to eight pure white eggs.

The Kingfisher's nest is not usually a very tidy place nor a very sweet-smelling one. Fish have bones and heads, and as it is a long way out to daylight, it could not be expected that the father and mother, constantly on the run to catch fish for their screaming young, would put out the garbage every day.

G.D.W.

THE WHIPPOORWILL

The Whippoorwill belongs to a family called goatsuckers, because certain members of the family were known to fly through flocks of goats and even between the legs of those animals. Goatherds with a taste for milk had to explain why the goats' udders were not always full at milking time. They took to blaming the loss on the birds, who really never touched a drop of milk and were only looking for insects.

The Whippoorwill of the United States is a fascinating bird with a throaty-whistled song which is supposed to sound like his name. The eastern Indians thought is sounded like "wi-ku-li" and that is what they called the bird. During the summer months the Whippoorwill repeats this call hundreds of times in succession. It is a wonderful thing to hear, but it is hard to sleep when its cry is going on.

The Whippoorwill is remarkable in that it builds no nest. A nest is not called a nest unless a bird has done some work on it. The Whippoorwill simply alights and lays her eggs without so much as moving a leaf or piece of grass. She lays two eggs on the ground and in spite of snakes, dogs, skunks, cats, and foxes, all of whom like eggs, manages to perpetuate her kind. Perhaps it helps that her young are of the kind which can run and hide under leaves as soon as they are hatched, thereby escaping their enemies. Whatever the reason, the Whippoorwill has been around for a long time and shows little sign of dying out where there are trees among which to lie dormant during the day.

THE NIGHTHAWK

The Nighthawk has become something of a "city slicker." On summer evenings he soars and dives over homes and office buildings, uttering his familiar nasal cry of "peent, peent." Though the female sometimes lays her two well-camouflaged eggs in a slight depression in an open space in woods or fields, or on a bare rock or gravelly beach where her own protective coloration makes her all but unnoticeable, Nighthawks have, in the century since flat roofs have been built in the United States, come to prefer rooftops.

It is interesting to note that the rooftop "nest" does not even stay in one place. During the incubation period, each time the female leaves the eggs to get her own food, and each time she alights upon them on her return, she rolls them along for an inch or two so that the chicks are hatched several feet away from the spot where the eggs were originally deposited. For about two weeks after the hatching the mother continues to tend the young, feeding them by regurgitation and protecting them with her own body from the heat of the summer sun as well as from the coolness of the night. Meanwhile, the young are learning to fly, and finally beginning to catch some of their own insect food.

Temperatures of 140 degrees have been recorded on rooftops which accommodate brooding Nighthawks, but though an occasional bird may succumb to the heat, he will not have to face any of the predatory animals which may attack those of his kind born on bare ground or rock.

THE FAIRY TERN

There is supposed to be a rule that the more dangerous a bird's life, the more eggs it will lay. The beautiful Fairy Tern seems not to have heard of this rule. It lays only one creamy egg, exquisitely marked with curly patterns of brown and sometimes a mist of pale purple among the curls. Moreover, it builds no nest at all. It sometimes lays its egg on bare rock, but most often balances it precariously in the crotch where a small branch joins a tree, or on a rough place in the bark of a branch where a twig has fallen off, sometimes within a few feet of the nests of other birds.

The mother straddles the egg when brooding, and when she has to get up and go away she backs off without disturbing the balance of the egg. On the islands of the Pacific where the Fairy Tern lives, winds of terrific force and high seas are not uncommon but it manages to raise enough young to survive. Perhaps this is because the young help out by being very gymnastic the minute they are hatched, hanging on to their cradle with beak and claw, defying all efforts of the wind and water to throw them off.

The Fairy Tern is one of the most beautiful of sea birds. It is, when fully grown, pure white with dark brown shining eyes which look larger than they are because they are surrounded by a ring of tiny black feathers. Its white wings are so delicate that the sun shines through them in flight.

90

THE HERRING GULL

The commonest "sea gull" of the North American coast is the Herring Gull, whose scientific name means "silvery." The Herring Gull nests in large colonies on small islands in the Atlantic off the northern New England coast and in parts of northern Europe. The colonies are so crowded that each bird has only a small territory he can call his own. While he defends this stoutly, he is peaceful enough if left alone, and goes in for quite a lot of ceremony.

Once he has picked a mate from among the eligible females in the public square of his colony, he sticks to her throughout his life. His courtship, like that of many birds, includes much play with sticks and straws and other materials which end up by being the materials of his mate's nest. Both the male and the female work at building the nest, although the male, feeling the need of calling attention to what he is doing by crying out, usually drops most of the material before he gets to the site. He sometimes sits in the nest before it is finished, as the female does, bending his head and squirming about to give finishing touches to the rim. This helps to round and smooth the cup in which, at intervals of about twenty four hours, three eggs are laid.

Gulls are great egg-eaters and will eat their own if they are found outside the nest, but not when they are in it.

THE OSPREY

The huge nest of an Osprey is large enough to contain several human instead of bird babies. Humans might, however, find it scratchy and uncomfortable, and they might be bothered by the smaller birds, usually grackles, that often build their own nests in the sides of the Osprey's.

Composed chiefly of rough sticks and branches, the nest may also include pieces of earth, cow dung, dried plants, and grasses or any convenient foreign material—newspapers, old furniture, rope, shells, or skeletons of dead birds. The softer materials are used for the lining. Some four or five feet in diameter and equally high, Osprey nests often weigh 500 to 1,000 pounds. They are usually found in trees, often dead trees, not far from the water, but sometimes telegraph poles or man-made platforms are used, and occasionally an Osprey will nest on the ground. They use the same nests year after year, sometimes—it is said—repairing and strengthening them in the fall for the next season.

The Osprey, or fish hawk, second only in size and wingspread to the eagle and gentlest of our hawks, is found all over the world. He is much admired for his nobility of appearance and skill at fishing. Unlike many fishermen, he never takes more than he needs to feed himself and his mate and the two or three young in the nest. It is an unforgettable sight to see him fly over lake, river, or sea, suddenly plunge down headfirst, and emerge a second later with a fish carried not in his mouth but in his sharp claws.

THE BRUSH TURKEY

Among the birds of Australia is a group known as *megapodes*, or "big feet," one of which is called the Brush Turkey. This bird, as if it remembered that birds are descended from reptiles, does not incubate its own eggs but lets nature do the job for it.

The Brush Turkey, which is about the size of a domestic chicken, builds a large mound of earth or sand many feet across, the center of which is hollowed out and filled with leaves and other vegetable matter. As the rainy season in Australia's Brush Turkey country corresponds with the bird's breeding season, the leaves in the mound are soon soaked. When they are, the birds cover them with a thin layer of sand and the female lays from four to eight eggs in a layer, their small ends pointing down and each some distance from the other. The eggs are then covered with sand and another layer of eggs deposited on that. This layer is in turn covered. After that, the male and female birds strut about the mound feeding and studying the weather. The wet vegetable matter in the mound rots and generates heat and the sun on top of it adds more. When the sun shines the birds scrape away a little sand to let more heat in. When it is cloudy they add sand to keep in the heat already there.

When the eggs hatch and the chicks find themselves buried alive, instinct tells them to start digging their way out through a foot and a half or two feet of mound.

96

THE ELF OWL

The deserts of southern Arizona, which although dry are too beautifully full of life to deserve the name of desert, shelter some remarkable creatures which are not found anywhere else in the world. Among these is the tiny Elf Owl, the world's smallest owl, not much larger than a good-sized sparrow. He is a night worker like most owls, living almost entirely on insects.

The Elf Owl is usually found in the great saguaro cactus, a very slow-growing, leafless tree covered with thorns and sometimes as much as forty feet high. The Elf Owl cannot dig his own nest hole but has an ally in the desert woodpecker, who has to dig holes in trees to get what he needs to eat and to make a nesting place for himself. The Elf Owl takes over an abandoned woodpecker hole and introduces it to his mate, who does her part by laying three tiny white eggs (sometimes only two, if the season is dry and food is scarce).

The Elf Owl can be seen during the day poking his comically severe face out of his hole among the spines of the cactus. If you try to get too near him he will strike a crazy pose with one wing thrust forward and his mouth open, as if he hoped you would mistake him for something other than an owl. Elf Owl pairs are very devoted to each other and are constantly "talking" as if they were really saying something.

THE TAILOR BIRD

We often hear people using the expression, "free as a bird." Yet birds, when you come to think of it, are really not free at all. They have to behave the way their inherited habits tell them to.

There is a very clever little yellow-green bird with a light breast living in India and southeastern Asia, called the Tailor Bird. The Tailor Bird is shaped something like a wren, only with a longer tail and a very sharp bill, but it is really related to the warblers. When the time for laying eggs comes around and the Tailor Bird has to find a place to put them, the parents remember that they are Tailor Birds and begin using their bills to punch a great many little holes along the two outer edges of a large leaf, preferably out near the end of a branch. The birds then thread lengths of grass or plant fiber through the holes and draw the edges of the leaf together. If there is not a large enough leaf handy, the Tailor Bird will sew two smaller ones together to make the nest cornucopia. The next step is to find a quantity of plant fluff or down and stuff it into the leaf. Within this ingenious nest the female then lays her eggs.

The construction of this nest is such a clever idea that it might be supposed that other birds would borrow it. They do not, because they are not "free" to. A bird is a prisoner of his habits. He can make only his own kind of nest.

100

THE SOCIAL WEAVER

It is impossible to say what makes some birds eager to nest by themselves, to stake out a claim to a region about their nest and fight to keep others of their kind—in some cases of any kind— away from it. All birds are not so exclusive. Many sea birds live in huge colonies and so do some land birds.

One quite extraordinary example of what in human beings would be city life is offered by one of the African weaver birds, a rather dull-looking variety called the Social Weaver. This astonishing bird lives in the plains of southern Africa in colonies of anywhere from fifty to a hundred birds. The surprising thing about these birds is that they all live within the same nest.

This nest is a kind of apartment house. It is built in a thorn tree, often completely covering the tree and looking like the thatched hut of a human African. The gigantic structure is sometimes ten or twelve feet high and six or eight feet wide and is made of what would be several wagon loads of grass. The bottom of the nest is flat and is pierced by many holes, each one leading to the nest of an individual pair of birds. These individual nests are comfortably lined and contain from three to five bluish-beige, brown-spotted eggs.

The Social Weavers are constantly adding to their apartment house and sometimes add so much, in the course of years, that the tree in which it is built falls down.

THE HORNERO

The Hornero, or red ovenbird, lives in Argentina, Paraguay, and Uruguay. He is not to be confused with the American ovenbird, which is a warbler. The Hornero is a friendly if noisy bird who likes to live near human habitation. He is a mixture of brown and reddish-brown and the male is just like the female with nothing fancy about him.

The Hornero's nest is actually much more like an oven than is the leafy shelter of our warbler ovenbird. It is made of mud, strengthened with horsehair, usually a foot in diameter, and weighs six or seven pounds. It is dome-shaped and divided into two rooms, one being an entrance hall and the other, separated from it by a mud partition, a nest-chamber where five white eggs are laid (and where the Argentine version of the cowbird often sneaks in an extra one).

W. H. Hudson, an English bird lover who lived for a long time in Argentina, tells a story of a pair of Horneros. One of the pair got caught in a rat trap which practically cut off the poor creature's legs. When the bird was released from the trap it flew up into its oven and bled to death in the nesting chamber. Its male, who seems to have been more practical than romantic, promptly chose another companion. Together these two sealed up the nesting chamber with mud pellets, still containing the dead bird, and immediately built a new two-room oven on top of the old one.

104

THE HORNBILL

The Hornbills are a strange tribe of mostly black-and-white, fairly large birds living in the jungles and thick forests of Asia and Africa. They all have very exaggerated beaks, thick and, as the name suggests, horny. They will eat almost anything, but they are especially fond of fruit. No one would call them attractive. They are, however, interesting because of their strange nesting habits, although in the true sense they do not build nests at all.

After courtship, a pair of Hornbills looks for a tree with a hole in it, perhaps forty or fifty feet above the ground. It has to be a large hole as the Hornbill is a large bird. Into this hole goes the female, bent upon laying her eggs, incubating them, and at the same time getting over the unpleasant business of molting, which involves shedding her wing and tail feathers and growing new ones.

By way of protecting her, the male bird, who does not shed his feathers at the same time, goes about down below, swallowing lumps of mud and clay which, mixed with his saliva, he regurgitates at the mouth of the tree hole. The female uses this to plaster up the entrance to the hole, leaving only a small slit through which she may be fed. This keeps her and her eggs safe from monkeys and monitor lizards until the chicks are born and she has grown a new set of feathers.

THE HONEY-GUIDE

The African Honey-guide is one of the few birds with a taste for honeycomb. Stories of how he finds bee trees were for a long time thought to be myths but have been thoroughly verified. The bird, once he has located a bee swarm, flits about in the vicinity until he finds someone whose attention he can attract—a man, if possible, or an African honey badger. He keeps flying nearer to the bee tree, calling every time he changes position. Eventually the man or badger sees the bees and either chops down the tree or opens up the hole to get at the honey. The bird sits waiting until the honey gatherer has gone and then comes down to eat the broken comb.

The Honey-guide is one of those birds who builds no nest of his own but gets other birds to work for him. The female Honey-guide lays an egg in the nest of another kind of bird and leaves this dangerous package to take care of itself, which it is well equipped to do. When hatched, the baby Honey-guide has two sharp hooks on the tip of his bill, one on the upper and one on the lower half. These the savage young one uses (while he is still featherless and his eyes are closed) to attack the young of the owner of the nest. After he has killed his fellow nestlings he loses the bill hooks and behaves like a normal bird. The mother of the dead nestlings feeds him as if nothing had happened.

108

THE BALD EAGLE

THE BALD EAGLE

The Bald Eagle, our national bird, is truly a majestic creature with a white head, neck, and tail and a body of dark lustrous brown. He is not bald, in the sense of having no feathers on his head, but only by virtue of the fact that his head is white.

The Bald Eagle is, for reasons on which all students of the subject are not agreed, becoming very scarce. His nests today are hard to find. Once seen, they are not easy to forget. The eyrie of the great American bird is remarkable for its size. One nest in a dead sycamore tree in western Pennsylvania measured nine feet deep by six feet wide. Some nests are said to weigh as much as two tons. One explanation of the size of the Bald Eagle's nest is in the fact that, unlike most birds—excepting some other birds of prey—the nest is the Eagle's home. The male and female of this bird usually mate for life, returning to the nest—if indeed they ever leave it for any great length of time—every year and adding to it each time they return. The nest is made of sticks—not mere twigs, but dead branches which may be as much as two inches in diameter, pushed and pulled into place one layer on top of another.

The Bald Eagle usually lays two eggs which hatch in about five weeks. The young develop slowly and are fed on fish and game by the devoted parents. The eaglets, having a large nest surface to move about on, use it as a sort of gymnasium to develop their muscles. Unlike most other birds, the young after their first flight from the nest return to it and share it for as much as three months with their parents. After that time, they are ready to go off on their own.

THE PALM SWIFT

The Swifts are remarkable birds that live more truly in the air than most birds, seldom leaving it except to rear their young or to sleep. They feed in flight, gather nesting materials while on the wing, and even mate in the air.

One of the most interesting of Swifts is the Old World Palm Swift. These black-backed birds live in Africa and Asia where, as their name suggests, they nest in palm trees. They do not build their nests on top of the palm branch. If they did, the hot sun would probably cook the eggs before they hatched. Instead, they use the underside of the leaf. All Swifts have a very sticky saliva which they use in nest-building. The Palm Swift lines the underside of the palm leaf with a flat, spoon-shaped cushion made of plant fibers and feathers caught from the air and glued together with gummy saliva. In the bowl of the "spoon" the female lays two eggs and fastens them to the nest with more saliva, which is just as well, since the nest is practically upside down. The bird clings to the nest by her claws while incubating the eggs. She cannot, as most birds do, turn the eggs over to give all sides an equal share of the warmth of her breast because they are glued to the nest. Nevertheless, the eggs hatch out into perfectly good Swifts that grip the nest with their claws until they are ready to fly.

THE PALM SWIFT

THE CAVE SWIFTLET

The family of Swifts has many interesting things about it, particularly its nesting habits. There is a kind of Swift living in southeastern Asia and the islands near it which nests in caves and is able not only to find its way about in the dark, but also to build its nest without the help of any light.

In the seventeenth century travelers from Asia brought to Europe samples of a strange kind of nest shaped like a new moon. These were not made of twigs or grass, but of a whitish substance which was almost transparent. The travelers, who were at first thought to be liars, said that these nests were made by a little bird like a swallow out of some substance gathered from the sea. The Chinese, it was reported, dissolved these nests in broth and found the resulting brew delicious.

It was not until long afterwards that the material of which these nests were made was identified and by that time it was so well established that they were edible that no one minded. The truth is that these remarkable objects were made almost entirely of the saliva of the Cave Swiftlet. It is little wonder that it is said that it takes five or six weeks to make a single nest. It is a great wonder that, since more than a thousand pounds of nests may be taken from a single cave in a season, there are any Swiftlets left to provide soup.

THE BOWERBIRD

The habits of birds which result in courtship, mating, nest-building, and the production of more birds sometimes lead in strange directions. There is a group of birds living in Australia and just north of it in the great island of New Guinea called Bowerbirds. These birds make nests in which to raise their young, but they apparently regard nesting as a mere duty rather than a pleasure. Another form of bird activity occupies them almost completely.

The males of this bird build the "bowers" which have given it its name. They are little playhouses made sometimes of cones of material piled about a central pole, sometimes of the stems of plants, even orchids, stood in rows two or three feet high and leaning against each other at the top to form a kind of tent. About this structure the ground is cleared, and sometimes ringed by a mound of moss. Near at hand are piled collections of bright objects—shells, the bones and skulls of small animals, colored pebbles, and flower heads. Sometimes these are arranged in borders lining little paths. Within the bower the male Bowerbird entertains his mate with bowing and dancing and juggling of the bright objects gathered there. It is as if the gathering of the material, which to most birds suggests nest-building, suggested to the Bowerbird nothing but play—play calculated to pass the time until the female is ready for mating and the insect population of the area has become great enough to provide food for young birds.

The nest, which is never in the bower area but in a tree or bush some distance away, is a quite ordinary nest, not even especially well made. It is built and tended by the female alone after the play-acting of courtship is over.

118

THE WHITE STORK

The great White Stork with his black wings and red feet is unknown in North America, but so close has he been to the lives of our European ancestors for centuries, even thousands of years, that it is almost as if we knew him. This huge, almost voiceless bird is only a summer resident in Europe, spending his winters in South Africa, but he seems to regard north Germany, Denmark, and the Netherlands as his home. Here he builds his great nests on chimneys, roof corners, windmills, church spires, and telegraph poles, returning from his winter wanderings to the same place every year.

Before bird migration was as well understood as it is now, it was thought that the Stork allowed smaller migrant birds, who could not stand such a long flight, to ride under the ample feathers of his back. The Stork's association with chimneys puts him in a class with Santa Claus and has led to his being thought of as the bringer of gifts to human households—in his case, babies.

The stork's own babies keep him busy enough without bothering about humans. In a great nest of sticks and reeds which weighs so much that householders often build platforms to support it, the female Stork lays three or four white eggs and raises her young with extremely careful attention until they are as much as two feet tall and can get out of their upper berths and fly away to the marshes after their own frogs. It is said that the Stork is actually more devoted to her nest than she is to her young.

A SELECTED BIBLIOGRAPHY

The following books are written primarily for adults and while some of them might, in part, be difficult for young people, they will widen the reader's field of interest and answer most questions arising out of the notes presented in these pages.

Allen, Arthur A. *The Book of Bird Life*. Princeton, N.J.: Van Nostrand, 1961.
> A simply written, beautifully illustrated, and fascinating account of bird life, with emphasis on courtship and nesting.

Bent, Arthur Cleveland. *Life Histories of North American Birds*. Washington: various dates.
> Bent's great work, published by the Smithsonian Institution in many volumes, some of which are out of print, has been reprinted in paperback by Dover Publications, Inc., New York.

Coward, T. A. *Birds and Their Young*. London: Gay and Hancock, 1923.
> A study of bird habits in connection with the breeding cycle. This book deals mostly with British birds, but gives an excellent background for the understanding of nesting.

Dugmore, A. Radclyffe. *Bird Homes*. New York: Doubleday, 1905.
> A fairly detailed and readable study of North American birds, their nesting habits, and their eggs. Well illustrated.

Fisher, James. *A History of Birds*. Boston: Houghton Mifflin, 1954.
> A small, well-written book giving an account of what men of various periods have known and written about birds and pointing out the manner in which birds as we know them have developed. The chapter on "Bird History" is especially interesting; though designed for university students, it will not prove difficult for any bright younger reader.

Headstrom, Richard. *Birds' Nests: A Field Guide.* New York: Washburn, 1949.

Headstrom's somewhat superficial work does give descriptions of nests not included in this present volume and suggests where they may be found.

Herrick, Francis Hobart. *The Home Life of Wild Birds.* New York: Putnam, 1901.
An old book, but one of the first to make a serious study of nesting birds. Many excellent photographs are included.

Pycraft, W. P. *A History of Birds.* London: Methuen & Co., Ltd., 1910.
More detailed and more simple than Fisher's history. Chapters X through XV are especially interesting.

Reed, Chester A. *North American Birds' Eggs.* New York: Doubleday, 1904.
Describes nests as well as eggs.

Thompson, Sir A. Landsborough. *A New Dictionary of Birds.* London: Thomas Nelson and Sons Ltd., 1964.
Thompson's is an invaluable, alphabetically arranged encyclopedia of all aspects of bird life.

INDEX

THE AUTHOR

RAYMOND HOLDEN is a native New Yorker with a great variety of interests. He is a director of Early Sites Foundation, a New England organization devoted to archaeological research, maintains a bird-banding station, and finds time to relax in his workshop doing carpentry work and mounting natural history specimens which he collects. He has been a close student of birds for many years and is a member of the American Ornithologists Union and the Cornell Laboratory of Ornithology.

Mr. Holden's writing is marked by variety also. His adult titles include THE MERRIMACK in the "Rivers of America" series and THE REMINDING SALT, a book of his own poetry. For young readers he has written SECRETS IN THE DUST, the story of archaeology, FAMOUS SCIENTIFIC EXPEDITIONS, FAMOUS FOSSIL FINDS, and other volumes.

A graduate of Princeton, Raymond Holden lives with his wife, Barbara, in Newport, New Hampshire.

THE ILLUSTRATOR

GRACE DEWITT is known for her original oil and watercolor paintings. Extensive exhibits in art galleries and one-woman showings have been recognized throughout New York, New Jersey and the Midwest. She received her B.A. degree from William Smith College in New York, attended Oberlin Conservatory of Music, and has done graduate work. She has been closely associated with young people, teaching art and music in elementary schools and as art director of the Park Ridge, New Jersey, public schools from 1957 to 1959. In 1967 Mrs. DeWitt organized a creative art workshop in Haworth, New Jersey, where she resides with her husband and three children.